classical chillout

PLATINUM EDITION

for solo piano

Chester Music
London/New York/Paris/Sydney/Copenhagen/Berlin/Madrid/Tokyo

Exclusive distributors:
Chester Music Limited
part of The Music Sales Group
14-15 Berners Street, London W1T 3LJ, UK.

Order No. CH68090
ISBN 978-1-84449-472-9
This book © Copyright 2004 by Chester Music Limited.

Compiled by Heather Ramage.
Additional music processed by Note-orious Productions Limited.
Additional music arranged by Jerry Lanning.

Printed in the United Kingdom.

Your Guarantee of Quality:

As publishers, we strive to produce every book to the highest commercial standards.
The music has been carefully designed to minimise awkward page turns
and to make playing from it a real pleasure.

Particular care has been given to specifying acid-free, neutral-sized paper
made from pulps which have not been elemental chlorine bleached.

This pulp is from farmed sustainable forests and was produced with special regard
for the environment. Throughout, the printing and binding have been planned to ensure
a sturdy, attractive publication which should give years of enjoyment.

If your copy fails to meet our high standards, please inform us
and we will gladly replace it.

www.musicsales.com

adagio of spartacus and phrygia

from *Spartacus*

By Aram Khachaturian

accel. poco a poco

rall.

a tempo

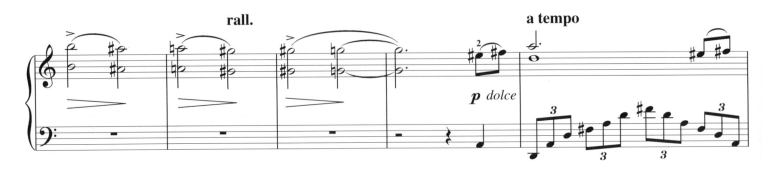

6

molto rit.

Lento

agnus dei

from *Requiem*

By Gabriel Fauré

Molto largo ($\quad$ = 40)

Tempo I

11

air
from *Water Music*

By George Frideric Handel

chorus of the hebrew slaves (va pensiero)

from *Nabucco*

By Giuseppe Verdi

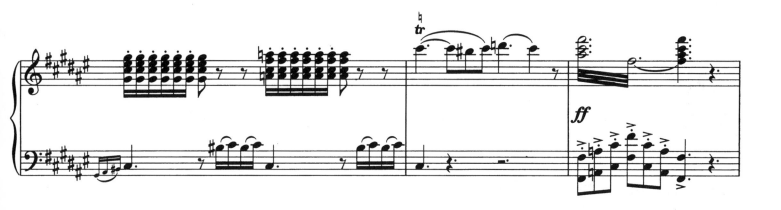

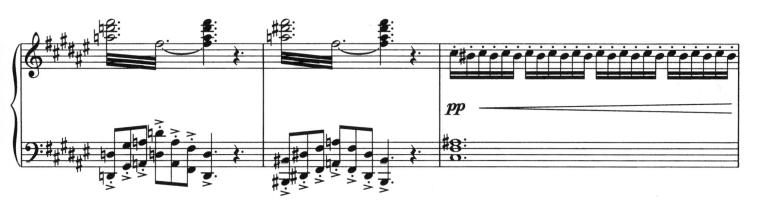

19

ave maria

By Franz Schubert

Moderato

the blue bird

By Charles Villiers Stanford

Larghetto tranquillo

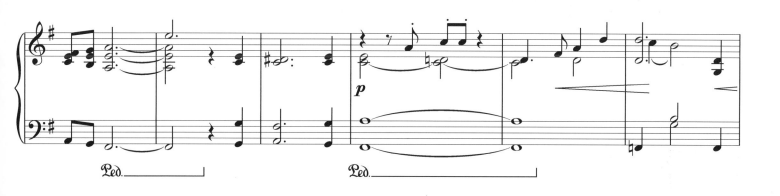

Più lento

from foreign lands and people

from *Scenes From Childhood*

By Robert Schumann

pavane
theme from *The Incredible Mrs Ritchie*

By Patrick Hawes

Moderately slow ♩ = 68

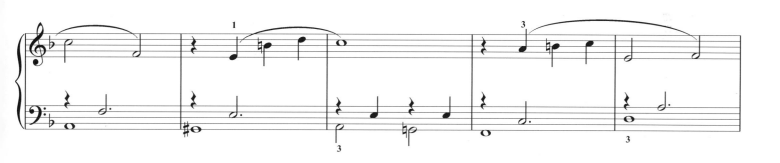

26

piano concerto no.2

(Larghetto)

By Frédéric Chopin

29

sonata pathétique, op.13
(Adagio Cantabile)

By Ludwig Van Beethoven

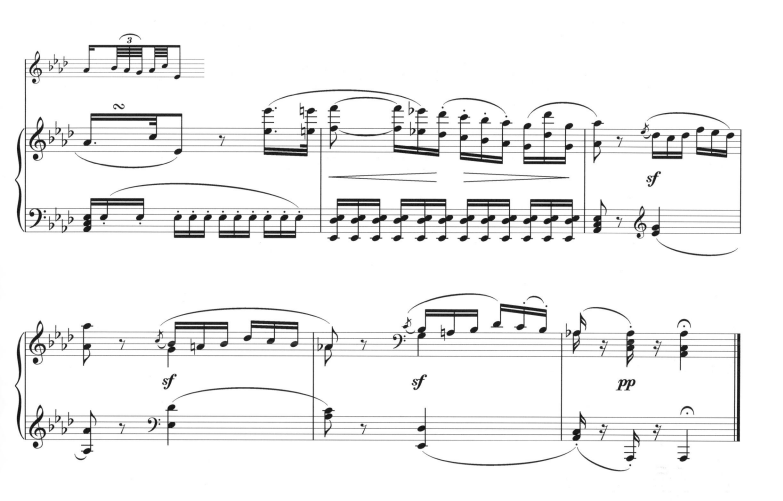

piano concerto no.1
(Opening Theme)

By Pyotr Ilyich Tchaikovsky

piano concerto no.21
'elvira madigan'
(Andante)

By Wolfgang Amadeus Mozart

40

43

rêverie

By Claude Debussy

Andantino sans lenteur

47

49

love theme from *romeo & juliet*

By Nino Rota

Slow and expressive

string quartet no.2
(Theme)

By Alexander Borodin

Andante ♩ = 60

cantabile ed espressivo

sleepers awake

from *Cantata No.140*

By Johann Sebastian Bach

Allegretto tranquillo

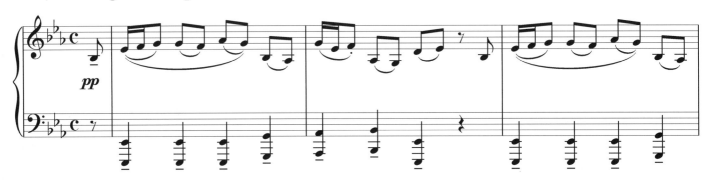

simile

sempre **pp**

sur le fil

from *Amelie*

By Yann Tiersen

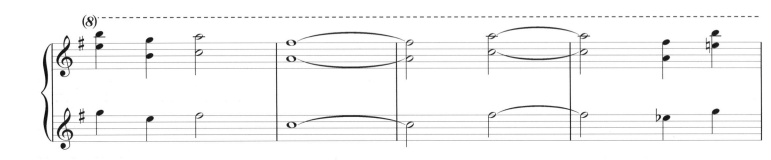

61

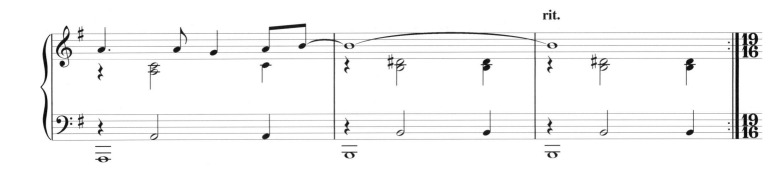

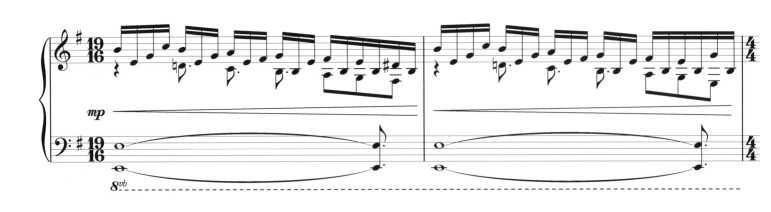

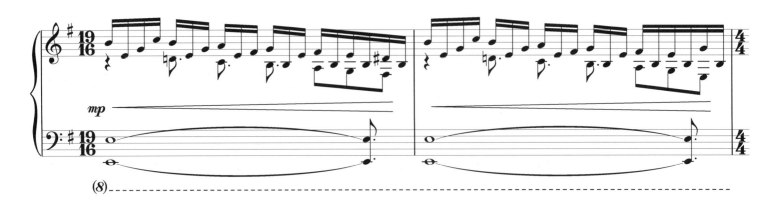

symphony no.3 in f major

(Poco Allegretto)

By Johannes Brahms

Poco allegretto

poco rit.

theme from *between strangers*

By Zbigniew Preisner

rit.   a tempo

meno mosso

dim.

Ped.

theme from *schindler's list*

By John Williams

Expressively

74

theme from *six feet under*

By Thomas Newman

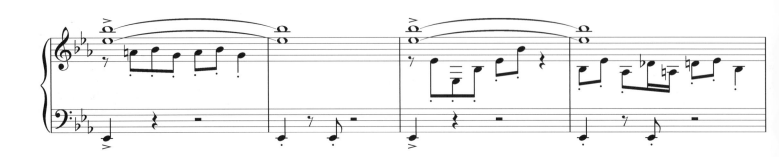

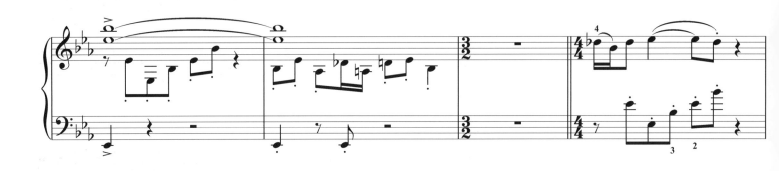

theme from *a summer place*

By Max Steiner

smoothly

1.

2.

L.H.

theme from *you only live twice*

Words by Leslie Bricusse
Music by John Barry

Moderately ♩ = 76

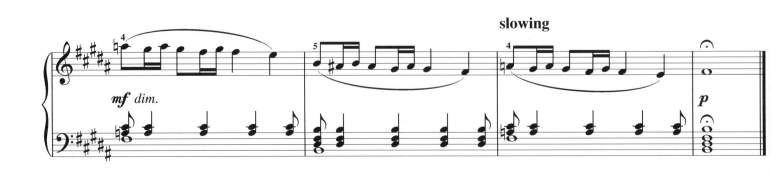

violin concerto in e minor
(Andante)

By Felix Mendelssohn

Andante ♪ = 96

to a wild rose

By Edward MacDowell

With simple tenderness

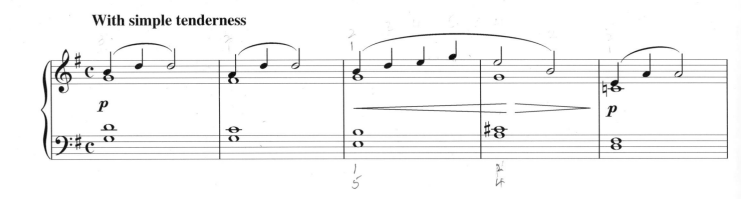

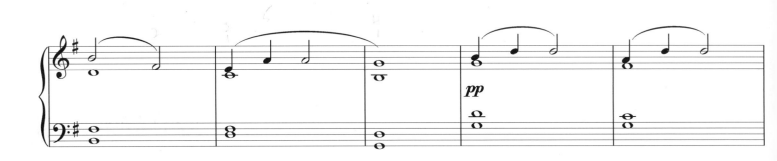

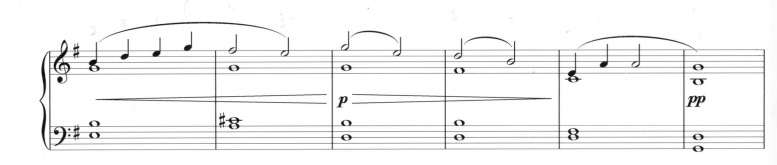

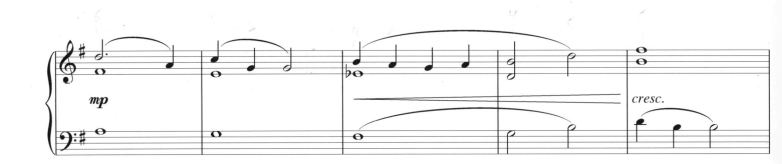

the universal

By Damon Albarn, Graham Coxon, Alex James & David Rowntree

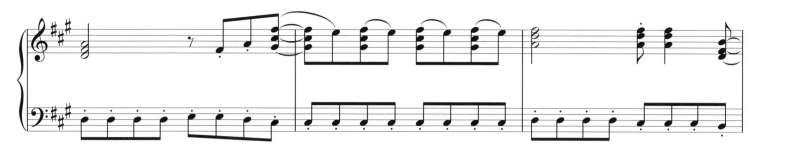

walking song

from Lifecycle (1996)

By Howard Blake

Semplice, tranquillo ($\quarternote$ = 96)

Other books for solo piano

CLASSIC ADS
22 classic themes and music made popular by T.V. adverts. Includes: Adagio for Strings (The Times), 633 Squadron (Zurich), Johnny and Mary (Renault Clio), Fields of Gold (Cancer Research).
Order No. CH65989

MOVIE HITS YOU'VE ALWAYS WANTED TO PLAY
30 of the best known themes and songs from the greatest films arranged for intermediate solo piano. Includes: American Beauty, Chocolat, Crouching Tiger Hidden Dragon, Moulin Rouge, and many more.
Order No. CH65439

CLASSICAL CHILLOUT
Sit down at the piano and chill out with some of the world's most soothing melodies. Includes: Clair de Lune (Debussy), Gymnopédie No.1 (Satie), Sarabande in D minor (Handel) and The Heart Asks Pleasure First from "The Piano" (Nyman).
Order No. CH64053

CLASSICAL CHILLOUT GOLD
Unwind with this great sequel to our best selling *classical chillout* containing 29 super cool piano favourites to play and enjoy. Includes: Adagio for Strings (Barber), The Lamb (Tavener), Pavane (Fauré)
Order No. CH66319

THE GOLD SERIES
A beautifully presented series of albums containing the most famous masterpieces from the world's greatest composers.

MOZART GOLD
Includes: A Musical Joke, Piano Concerto No.21 'Elvira Madigan', Serenade in B♭ 'Gran Partita' and Symphony No.40 in G minor.
Order No. CH65505

BEETHOVEN GOLD
Includes: Symphony No.5, Für Elise, Minuet in G and the 'Moonlight' Sonata.
Order No. CH65670

CHOPIN GOLD
Includes: All famous waltzes, nocturnes, preludes and mazurkas as well as excerpts from Piano Concerto No.1, Ballade in G minor and Sonata No.2 in B♭ Minor.
Order No. CH65681

TCHAIKOVSKY GOLD
Includes: 1812 Overture, plus music from The Nutcracker, Sleeping Beauty and Swan Lake.
Order No. CH65692

For more information on these and the thousands of other titles available from Chester Music and Music Sales, please contact:

Music Sales Limited
Newmarket Road, Bury St Edmunds, Suffolk, IP33 3YB.
Tel: 01284 702600. Fax: 01284 768301.
www.musicsales.com